Ten Short Stories

The Earthquake
The Flood
The Volcano
The Pandemic
The Fire
The Hurricane
The Tsunami
The Avalanche
The Drought
The Heatwave

By Chris Charlton

The Earthquake

It was a beautiful spring day in Valdivia, Chile, on May 22, 1960. Fernando and his wife Roberta were sitting in their living room, chatting about their future plans. They were talking about the construction of a new house and how excited they were about it. Suddenly, the earth began to shake. The ground beneath them trembled with such force that it seemed as if the whole world was coming apart.

"Oh my God, what's happening?" Roberta shouted as she clung to Fernando.

"It's an earthquake!" Fernando shouted back as he tried to hold on to Roberta and keep them both from falling.

The earthquake lasted for several minutes, and when it was over, Fernando and Roberta were trapped in their house. The walls had caved in, and there was no way out.

"Roberta, are you okay?" Fernando asked as he checked on her.

"Yes, I'm okay, but what are we going to do?" Roberta asked, her voice shaking.

"We need to stay calm and wait for help," Fernando replied.

Fernando and Roberta were trapped in their house for four days without food or water. They tried to conserve their energy and hope for the best. However, the local authorities were slow to react, and the local people were very unhappy.

"Why isn't anyone coming to help us?" Roberta asked, her voice filled with desperation.

"I don't know, but we need to keep hope alive," Fernando replied as he held her hand.

The waiting was torturous, and the couple could hear the sounds of destruction and chaos outside. They could hear the cries of those who had lost their homes and loved ones.

"This is a disaster, and the local authorities are doing nothing to help the people," one local resident shouted in anger.

"We need food, water, and medical supplies, but no one is taking us seriously," another resident added.

Finally, after four long days, Fernando and Roberta were rescued. They were taken to a shelter, where they were given food, water, and medical attention. They were shocked by the extent of the damage caused by the earthquake. Two million people had become homeless, and the city was in shambles.

"I can't believe what has happened to our city," Roberta said, tears streaming down her face.

"I know, it's a tragedy, but we are lucky to be alive," Fernando replied as he hugged her.

The couple started to rebuild their lives, but the memories of the earthquake would stay with them forever. The local authorities were criticized for their slow response and lack of help for the people. The earthquake was a wake-up call for the government to be better prepared for future natural disasters.

Despite the tragedy, the people of Valdivia came together to rebuild their city. They helped each other to clean up the rubble and find new homes. The government finally stepped up and provided assistance to those in need.

"We may have lost our homes and possessions, but we still have each other," Roberta said as she held Fernando's hand.

"Yes, and we will rebuild a better and stronger city," Fernando replied with a smile.

And that's exactly what they did. The city of Valdivia was rebuilt, and it became a symbol of resilience and hope. The earthquake was a tragic event, but it brought the people of Valdivia closer together. They learned the importance of working together and supporting each other in times of crisis.

Years passed, and the city was thriving once again. The new houses were built to withstand earthquakes, and the government had a plan in place to respond quickly in the event of another disaster. Fernando and Roberta's new house was a testament to their determination and strength. They had overcome the odds and made a new life for themselves.

Fernando and Roberta were often asked to speak about their experience during the earthquake. They shared their story with the hope of inspiring others and reminding the people of Valdivia of the importance of being prepared for natural disasters.

"We went through a tragedy, but we came out stronger because of our community," Fernando would say during his speeches. "We learned that in times of crisis, it's important to support each other and never give up hope," Roberta would add.

Their story touched the hearts of many, and they became symbols of hope and resilience in the city of Valdivia. The earthquake may have been a tragedy, but it brought out the best in the people of Valdivia and showed the world the power of the human spirit.

Fernando and Roberta lived the rest of their lives in the city of Valdivia, and their story was passed down from generation to generation. The earthquake was a reminder of the fragility of life and the importance of being prepared for natural disasters. But it was also a testament to the strength and resilience of the human spirit. The people of Valdivia never forgot the tragedy, but they also never forgot the love and hope that brought them together. The city of Valdivia continued to thrive, and the memory of Fernando and Roberta's story inspired the people to always be ready to face challenges with determination and resilience.

The Flood

Rita watched in horror as the water rose higher and higher, engulfing everything in its path. She clutched her four children tightly, trying to protect them from the raging floodwaters that threatened to sweep them away. They were trapped on the roof of their house, surrounded by the churning river that had once been their peaceful neighborhood.

"Mom, what's going to happen to us?" cried her youngest daughter, Maria.

Rita tried to put on a brave face, but the truth was, she was scared out of her mind. She had already lost her husband John and her mother Lucia to the flood. And now, they were surrounded by crocodiles, circling their house, waiting for their next meal.

"We have to stay calm, my love," Rita said, trying to reassure Maria. "The government will come to rescue us soon."

But even as she spoke the words, Rita wasn't sure she believed them. The local authorities had been slow to react, and she was worried that they might not come in time to save her and her children.

For the next four days, Rita and her children huddled on the roof, trying to keep dry and safe from the crocodiles. They were running low on food and water, and Rita was starting to lose hope.

"Why isn't anyone coming to save us?" cried her son, Jose. "We're going to die here."

Rita tried to comfort him, but she was starting to feel the same way. The water was still rising, and the crocodiles were becoming more and more aggressive.

"We have to have faith, my love," Rita said, trying to keep her voice steady. "The government will come for us. They have to."

But as the days passed, Rita's faith was waning. She was starting to fear that they would never be rescued, and that they would be trapped on the roof forever.

Just when all hope seemed lost, Rita heard the sound of a rescue boat approaching. She screamed for help, and the boat quickly came to their rescue. The children were loaded onto the boat first, and then Rita.

"Thank you, thank you so much," Rita cried, tears streaming down her face. "I thought we were going to die."

The rescuers nodded sympathetically. They had seen so much destruction and loss in the aftermath of the flood.

"We're just doing our job," one of the rescuers said. "But I'm glad we could help you and your children."

The flood had been one of the worst natural disasters in the history of the Philippines, leaving many people homeless. Rita and her children were among the lucky ones who had been rescued, but they had lost everything they owned.

"What are we going to do now?" Maria asked, her eyes wide with fear.

Rita took a deep breath. She was a strong woman, and she knew that she would have to be strong for her children.

"We'll start over," she said firmly. "We'll rebuild our lives, and we'll be stronger for it."

And that's exactly what they did. Rita and her children worked tirelessly to rebuild their lives, and they never forgot the love and courage that had helped them survive the flood. They were a testament to the strength of the human spirit, and an inspiration to others who had lost everything in the disaster.

Years passed, and the city of Manila was thriving once again. Rita's children had grown up and started families of their own, but they never forgot the lessons they had learned during the flood. They were grateful for the strength and resilience their mother had shown during that difficult time, and they were determined to pass those values on to their own children.

"Mom, do you remember the flood?" Jose asked one day as he visited Rita at her home.
Rita smiled. "Of course I do. It was one of the toughest times in my life, but it also taught me so much about courage and hope."
"I'm just glad we made it through," Jose said, giving his mother a hug. "I don't know what I would have done without you."

Rita hugged her son back, feeling grateful for her family and the love they shared. She looked out the window, remembering the frightening days they had spent on the roof, surrounded by the churning floodwaters and the circling crocodiles. But she also remembered the rescue boat that had come to their aid, and the courage and determination that had helped her and her children survive.

"I'm proud of us," Rita said, her voice filled with emotion. "We made it through one of the toughest times in our lives, and we came out stronger for it."

And with those words, Rita knew that the flood would always be a part of her story, but it would not define her. She was a survivor, and her strength and resilience would live on in her children and her grandchildren for generations to come.

The Volcano

Franco and his son Paulo were working in their fields near the base of Mount Vesuvius when they noticed a strange plume of smoke rising from the summit. They looked up, their eyes drawn to the towering volcano, and they felt a sense of unease in the pit of their stomachs.

"Paulo, do you see that?" Franco asked, pointing to the smoke.

Paulo nodded, his expression tense. "It looks like the volcano is erupting."

They watched in stunned silence as a massive ash cloud rose from the summit, followed by a river of lava cascading down the mountain's slopes. Franco and Paulo felt a jolt of fear as they realized that the eruption was headed straight for them.

"We have to get to safety!" Franco shouted, grabbing Paulo's arm.

Paulo and Franco ran for their lives, their feet pounding the earth as they raced back to the nearby village. But when they arrived, they found the streets in chaos. People were screaming, buildings were collapsing, and ash was falling like rain from the sky.

Paulo searched desperately for his wife and daughter, but he couldn't find them anywhere. The ash cloud was getting thicker, making it difficult to see, and he knew that time was running out. He stumbled into a crumbling building, his heart pounding with fear, and he saw his wife's lifeless body lying on the ground. Paulo fell to his knees, tears streaming down his face, as he realized that he had lost everything.

Franco and Paulo managed to find shelter in a cave near the mountain, and they huddled there for two weeks, surviving on fruit and the occasional rabbit that Paulo was able to hunt. They were safe from the ash and the lava, but they were also cut off from the rest of the world, with no way of knowing what was happening outside their cave.

"We have to find a way out of here," Franco said, his voice low and strained. "We can't stay here forever."

Paulo nodded, his eyes filled with determination. "I'll find a way out," he said. "I promise."

Finally, after two weeks of waiting, a rescue party arrived at the cave, led by a group of soldiers from the nearby city of Naples. Paulo and Franco were overjoyed to see that help had arrived, and they followed the soldiers back to the city, where they found that the devastation from the eruption was even worse than they had imagined.

"We have nothing left," a soldier told them, his voice filled with sorrow. "The ash and the lava destroyed everything in their path."

Paulo looked around at the ruined city, tears streaming down his face, as he remembered his wife and daughter, who had lost their lives in the eruption. He felt a sense of anger and frustration, knowing that the local authorities had been slow to react to the disaster.

"Why did this have to happen?" Paulo asked, his voice filled with emotion. "Why weren't the authorities prepared?"

In the years that followed the eruption of Mount Vesuvius, Franco and Paulo worked to rebuild their lives, determined to honor the memory of their loved ones. They became symbols of strength and resilience in the face of disaster, and their story inspired others to persevere in the face of adversity.

"We may have lost everything, but we didn't lose hope," Franco said, looking back on those difficult days. "We survived the eruption, and we will continue to survive, no matter what comes our way."

Their story became a part of the historical record, and the memory of the eruption of Mount Vesuvius in 79 AD lived on, a testament to the power and unpredictability of nature, and the resilience of the human spirit. The city of Pompeii was eventually rediscovered, and its ruins became a popular tourist destination, attracting millions of visitors every year from all over the world.

Despite the loss and destruction caused by the eruption, the people of Pompeii continued to live and thrive, their spirits unbroken by the disaster that had taken so much from them. They carried on, their lives a testament to the resilience of the human spirit in the face of even the greatest disasters.

"We may have lost our homes and our loved ones, but we have not lost our spirit," Paulo said, as he looked out at the rebuilt city of Pompeii. "We will continue to rebuild and to carry on, because that is what it means to be human."

The Pandemic

It all started in a market in Wuhan, China, where a new virus was first detected. The virus spread quickly, and soon cases were reported across the country. The rest of the world soon followed suit, closing their borders to China in a desperate attempt to slow the spread of the virus.

"This is not a time for panic," Dr. Pleats, a renowned scientist, said in a press conference. "We must work together to find a solution to this global crisis."

As more and more cases were reported, the world was forced into lockdown. People were working from home, businesses were closing, and life as we knew it was changing rapidly. Despite the measures being taken, the virus continued to spread, and people were dying all around the world.

"We must all do our part to stop the spread of this virus," Dr. Pleats said. "Stay at home, wash your hands, and wear a mask. We will get through this together."

Dr. Pleats worked tirelessly, day and night, to find a solution to the pandemic. She spent hours in her laboratory, running experiments and analyzing data, determined to find a cure.

"I will not rest until I have found a way to stop this virus," she declared.

After months of hard work, Dr. Pleats finally had a breakthrough. She had created a new vaccine that showed promise in fighting the virus. The world held its breath as the vaccine was tested on thousands of people, and the results were overwhelmingly positive.

"This is the moment we have been waiting for," Dr. Pleats said. "We are finally on the road to recovery."

However, Dr. Pleats' joy was short-lived. Just one week before the vaccine was set to be released to the public, she fell ill with COVID-19. Despite the best efforts of the medical community, she passed away just a few days later.

"Dr. Pleats was a true hero," one of her colleagues said at her funeral. "She devoted her life to finding a cure for this virus, and she will always be remembered for her bravery and her dedication to helping others."

Despite Dr. Pleats' loss, the vaccine she created was a success, and the world slowly began to return to normal. Borders opened, businesses reopened, and people started to regain a sense of hope and optimism.

"We have been through a difficult time," one survivor of the pandemic said. "But we have come out the other side, stronger and more united than ever before. We will never forget the sacrifices of those we have lost, but we will always carry their memory with us as we move forward."

The pandemic had left its mark on the world, and the memories of the tragedy would linger for years to come. But in the end, it was the spirit of resilience and determination that would triumph, as the world moved forward, stronger and more united than ever before.

The Fire

Dwayne was a proud farmer from the rural countryside of Australia. His family had lived on their farm for generations, and he loved working the land and caring for his animals. But in the summer of 2019, everything changed. A massive bushfire swept through the region, leaving destruction and chaos in its wake.

As the fire approached, Dwayne tried to save his farm and his animals. He raced around, trying to herd the cattle and sheep to safety, but the smoke was so thick that he could barely see. The heat was intense, and he could feel the blistering flames all around him. He knew that he had to get out of there, but the roads were blocked and he was trapped.

"I can't believe this is happening," he muttered to himself. "Everything I've worked for, everything I love, it's all just... gone."

For days, Dwayne was trapped on his farm, surrounded by the inferno. He was running out of food and water, and he could feel the exhaustion setting in. Just as he was about to lose all hope, he heard the sound of a helicopter overhead. He looked up and saw a rescue team hovering above him, lowering a rope ladder.

"Thank God," he said, tears streaming down his face. "They've come for me."

Dwayne clambered up the ladder and into the helicopter, grateful to be rescued but heartbroken at the destruction he had seen. As the helicopter flew away, he looked down at the blazing inferno below and whispered, "Goodbye, home."

After the rescue, Dwayne was taken to a hospital in Sydney. He was treated for smoke inhalation and minor burns, but he was otherwise okay. As he recovered, he began to realize that his old life was gone forever. His farm and his animals were destroyed, and he had no reason to go back.

So he decided to start a new life in Sydney. He found a job and a place to live, but he couldn't shake the memories of his old home. He missed the rolling hills and the sound of the animals. He missed the peace and quiet of the countryside.

"I don't belong here," he said to his new friends in Sydney. "I'm just a farmer at heart. I miss my home."

Although Dwayne tried to make the best of his new life in Sydney, he couldn't help but feel a sense of longing for his old home. He thought about it every day, and he often found himself staring out the window, lost in thought.

One day, he decided that he needed to go back and see what was left of his farm. He took a train back to the countryside and walked to where his farm used to be. When he got there, he was shocked by what he saw. The land was black and barren, and there was nothing left of his house or his animals.

"It's gone," he said, tears rolling down his cheeks. "Everything's gone."

But as he stood there, surrounded by the ashes of his old life, he realized that the memories were still there. He would always remember the sound of the animals and the smell of the land. He would always remember the happiness and peace that he had felt there.

"I may have lost my home, but I'll never lose my memories," he said, smiling through his tears. "And one day, I'll find a new place to call home."

Dwayne returned to Sydney with a renewed sense of purpose. He knew that he couldn't bring back his old home, but he was determined to make a new life for himself. He started volunteering at a local animal rescue center, helping care for animals that had been affected by the bushfires.

He found joy in working with the animals and he felt like he was making a difference. Slowly but surely, he began to build a new community for himself in Sydney. He made new friends and started to feel like he belonged.

One day, a woman named Sarah came to the animal rescue center. She was a farmer who had also lost her home in the bushfires. Dwayne and Sarah bonded over their shared experiences, and soon they became good friends.

As Dwayne and Sarah continued to work together at the animal rescue center, they realized that they had feelings for each other. They started dating, and soon they were talking about starting a new farm together.

They found a piece of land in the countryside that had escaped the bushfires and decided to start a new farm there. They worked hard to build their new home, and soon they had a thriving farm filled with animals and crops.
Dwayne and Sarah were happy, and they felt like they had finally found a place to call home. They had each other, a new community, and a new purpose. They looked forward to a bright future filled with love and happiness.

Years passed, and Dwayne and Sarah's farm became a symbol of resilience and hope in the aftermath of the bushfires. They had overcome the tragedy of losing their homes and had created a new life for themselves.

Their story inspired others who had been affected by the bushfires, and they became known as the "farmers of hope." They continued to work hard, care for their animals, and give back to their community.

Their legacy lived on, and their story was passed down from generation to generation, reminding people that it is possible to rise from the ashes and find happiness and hope after even the darkest of tragedies.

The Hurricane

It was the summer of 1984 and Florida was in the midst of a hurricane season. Archie and Catherine were a young couple who lived in a small coastal town with their two children. They were used to the occasional storm, but they had never experienced anything like this.

As the winds began to pick up and the rain started to pour, they knew they needed to take action. They gathered their children and some essentials, and headed to the local shelter.

"This is it, the big one," Archie said to Catherine as they huddled in the shelter with their children.

The storm raged on for hours, battering their town with strong winds and heavy rain. When it finally passed, Archie and Catherine stepped outside to survey the damage.

"Oh my God," Catherine whispered as she looked around. "Everything is gone."

The hurricane had destroyed everything in its path. Their home, their neighbors' homes, and their entire town was nothing but rubble. They had lost everything, including their children. They were homeless, and the government refused to help them. They turned to alcohol and drugs as a means of coping, and the once happy couple became distant and disconnected from each other.

"We had it all, and now we have nothing," Catherine said, taking a drink from a bottle of whiskey. "What's the point of living?"

Archie shook his head. "We have each other," he replied, though his words lacked conviction. "We'll get through this."

But as the days turned into weeks and the weeks turned into months, their situation only worsened. They slept on the streets, relying on the kindness of strangers for food and shelter. They were constantly exposed to the elements, and their health suffered as a result.

One day, Catherine collapsed on the street. She was rushed to the hospital, but it was too late. The years of living on the streets and the abuse of alcohol and drugs had taken their toll, and she died.

Archie was devastated. He was consumed by grief and regret, and he spiraled further into addiction. He no longer cared about life or about himself. He was just existing, day by day.
"Why did you leave me, Catherine?" he said, talking to her photo. "I can't do this without you."

For the next ten years, Archie lived on the streets. He had given up on life, and he was just surviving. He was lost and alone, with no one to turn to.

But one day, two people named Gary and Barbara approached him. They were volunteers for a local homeless shelter, and they saw something in Archie that they wanted to help.

"Hi there," Gary said, smiling at Archie. "We'd like to help you get back on your feet."

Archie was skeptical at first. He had heard these promises before, and he had been disappointed time and time again. But something about Gary and Barbara was different. They were genuine, and they seemed to genuinely care.

"What do you want from me?" Archie asked.

"We just want to help you," Barbara replied. "We know what it's like to hit rock bottom, and we want to be there for you."

Over the next few months, Gary and Barbara helped Archie get back on his feet. They provided him with food, shelter, and support, and they helped him overcome his addiction. They showed him kindness and compassion, and they helped him regain his self-worth.

Archie's life was forever changed by the help of Gary and Barbara. He was no longer homeless, and he had a new purpose in life. He began to work, and he even started volunteering at the homeless shelter where he had received help. He wanted to pay it forward and help others who were in the same situation that he once was.

"I never thought I'd be able to turn my life around," Archie said, smiling. "But with the help of Gary and Barbara, I was able to. They gave me hope when I had none, and they helped me see that there was a future for me."

Archie may have lost everything in the hurricane, but he had gained something even more valuable. He had a new life, and a new sense of purpose. He would always be grateful for the help he received from Gary and Barbara, and he would always be reminded that there was hope, even in the darkest of times.

The Tsunami

The year was 2004 and it was a beautiful day in Indonesia. The sun was shining and the birds were singing. People were going about their daily business, but little did they know that in a matter of minutes, their lives would change forever.

At around 9 am, a massive earthquake struck the Indian Ocean, generating a powerful tsunami that swept across the Indonesian coast, devastating everything in its path.

"I remember the ground shaking beneath my feet," said 32-year-old Sujanto, a fisherman from the small village of Cianjur. "I knew something was wrong, but I never expected this. The wave was huge, it must have been at least 10 meters tall."

The tsunami caused widespread destruction in Indonesia. Homes, buildings, and infrastructure were completely destroyed, leaving thousands of people homeless and without access to basic necessities like food and water.

"My children, my wife, and my home were all gone in an instant," said Sujanto, tears streaming down his face. "I felt like I had lost everything."

Sujanto, like many others, was in a state of shock. He wandered through the debris-filled streets, searching for any sign of his family. He called out their names, but there was no answer.
"I searched for days, but I couldn't find them," said Sujanto, his voice breaking. "I was scared that they were gone forever."

As the days passed, the government and aid organizations set up makeshift shelters for those who had lost their homes. Sujanto was grateful for the roof over his head, but the thought of his missing family never left him.

"I had nowhere else to go, so I stayed at the shelter," said Sujanto. "But I felt so alone, like I was the only one left in the world."

After several weeks of searching, Sujanto finally received word that his family had been found. They were being treated at a local hospital for their injuries, but they were alive.
Sujanto rushed to the hospital and was overjoyed to be reunited with his wife and children. They hugged and cried, grateful to be together again.

"I thought I had lost them forever," said Sujanto, tears of happiness streaming down his face. "But they were alive and that was all that mattered."

Despite their joyous reunion, Sujanto and his family faced a new problem: they had nowhere to live. Their home was gone, and they had no means of rebuilding it.

"We were starting from scratch," said Sujanto. "But we had each other and that was enough."
With the help of the government and aid organizations, Sujanto and his family were eventually able to find a new place to call home. They worked hard to rebuild their lives and slowly but surely, their strength and hope were restored.

"The tsunami may have taken everything from us, but it couldn't take away our love and our determination," said Sujanto. "We will always remember what happened, but we will not let it define us. We will keep moving forward."

The 2004 tsunami was one of the deadliest natural disasters in history, killing over 200,000 people in Indonesia alone. But despite the overwhelming loss and destruction, the survivors, like Sujanto and his family, showed incredible resilience and strength in the face of tragedy. They picked up the pieces of their lives and moved forward, never forgetting the ones they lost and always remembering the importance of family and love.

Years passed and Sujanto's family grew. His children went to school and got jobs, and Sujanto continued to fish, just like he did before the tsunami. They lived in their small village and continued to rebuild their community.

One day, Sujanto's oldest son came to him with an idea. He wanted to build a memorial for all those who lost their lives in the tsunami, a place where people could come to remember and pay their respects.

Sujanto was proud of his son and he immediately got to work. They worked together, with the help of the rest of the community, and soon the memorial was built. It was a simple structure, made of stone and wood, but it held great meaning.

"This memorial is not just for those who lost their lives in the tsunami, but for all those who have suffered and survived," said Sujanto during the dedication ceremony. "It is a symbol of hope and resilience, a reminder that no matter what life throws our way, we can always pick ourselves up and move forward."
And so, every year on the anniversary of the tsunami, Sujanto and his family, along with the rest of the community, gather at the

memorial to pay their respects and remember those who were lost. They light candles, lay flowers, and share stories, keeping the memories of the tragedy alive, but also celebrating the strength and resilience of the human spirit.

"The tsunami may have taken so much from us, but it also gave us something," said Sujanto. "It gave us the chance to come together, to support one another, and to rebuild. And for that, we will always be grateful."

The Avalanche

Zac was 18 years old, and he was an avid climber. He had been climbing since he was a little boy, and he loved the adrenaline rush that came with scaling a mountain. So, when his friend, Dave, invited him to climb Mount Blanc, he jumped at the opportunity. They were both experienced climbers and had done several climbs together before, but they were aware of the dangers that came with climbing such a massive mountain. They trained for weeks, making sure they were physically and mentally prepared for the climb. Finally, the day arrived, and they set off early in the morning, eager to reach the summit. The climb was going well, and they were making good progress. They were chatting and laughing, enjoying the beautiful scenery around them. But suddenly, without warning, an avalanche hit. Zac and Dave were caught in the middle of it, and they were swept away by the force of the snow.

Zac woke up, disoriented and confused. He was lying in a small crevice, surrounded by snow and ice. He looked around and saw that Dave was lying next to him, unconscious. Zac tried to shake Dave awake, but he didn't respond. Zac's heart sank as he realized that Dave was not breathing. He tried to revive him, but it was too late. Dave was gone. Zac was stranded, alone on the mountain, with no food or water. He had no way of communicating with the outside world and no way of getting down the mountain. He was in a dire situation, and he knew that he had to think fast if he wanted to survive.

Days passed, and Zac's situation became more desperate. He was hungry and thirsty, and he knew that he had to do something drastic if he wanted to survive. He thought about eating the snow, but he knew that it would only make him more dehydrated. Finally, in a moment of desperation, he realized that the only option he had was to eat Dave's body. He was horrified at the thought, but he knew that it was his only chance of survival. He took a deep breath and started to cut off pieces of flesh from Dave's body. He was crying as he ate, feeling guilty and ashamed for what he was doing. But he knew that it was a matter of life and death, and he had no choice but to continue.

After one week, Zac was finally rescued. He was weak and exhausted, but he was alive. He was taken to a hospital, where he was treated for dehydration and malnutrition. He was questioned by the police about what had happened on the mountain, and he told them the truth about how he had been forced to eat Dave's body in order to survive. The news of what had happened on the mountain spread quickly, and Zac became a controversial figure. Some people praised him for his bravery and resourcefulness, while others condemned him for what they saw as a horrific act.

After his recovery, Zac went back home to his family. He was still haunted by the memories of what had happened on the mountain, and he felt guilty for what he had done. He tried to go back to his normal life, but he found that he couldn't. He was afraid to climb again, and he was filled with a sense of dread every time he thought about it. So, he made the difficult decision to give up climbing for good. He never climbed again, and instead, he focused on moving forward with his life.

Years went by, and Zac eventually found peace with what had happened on the mountain. He realized that he had done what he had to do in order to survive, and he was proud of himself for being able to overcome such a difficult situation. He started a new chapter in his life, and he found new passions and interests. He got married and had children, and he was grateful for the love and support of his family. One day, his son asked him about his experience on the mountain. Zac told him the story, leaving out none of the details. When he finished, his son looked at him with awe and said, "You're a hero, Dad." Zac smiled, and for the first time in a long time, he felt a sense of pride. "I'm no hero," he replied. "I just did what I had to do to survive." And with that, Zac finally found closure, and he was able to put the past behind him and move forward with his life. He lived a long and happy life, always remembering the lesson he learned on the mountain: that sometimes, in order to survive, we have to do things that are hard and that we never thought we would have to do.

The Drought

The sun was shining bright and hot, but it brought no joy to the people of Uganda. For months, the country had been experiencing a severe drought that had caused crops to fail and water sources to dry up. The people were struggling to find enough food and water to survive, and many were starting to die from hunger and thirst.

Cedric was an 8-year-old boy who lived with his family in a small village in Uganda. They were farmers, and they relied on their crops to provide food and income for their family. But the drought had taken everything from them.

Cedric remembered the day his father had come back from the fields, tears in his eyes. "The crops have failed," he said. "We have nothing left to eat." Cedric's mother had started to cry, and his little sister had clung to her leg.

Days turned into weeks, and Cedric's family grew weaker and weaker. They ate what little food they had left, but it was not enough to sustain them. One by one, Cedric's family members started to die. First, it was his little sister, then his mother, and finally, his father. Cedric was left alone in the world.

Cedric was scared and alone, but he knew he had to find food and water if he wanted to survive. He left his village and started to wander the countryside, searching for anything that might sustain him.

At first, Cedric drank the milk from the cows he came across, but they too were suffering from the drought and soon died. He started to eat plants and insects, anything that he could find to keep himself alive.

One month after his family had died, Cedric was barely able to speak or move. He had become weak from hunger and thirst, and he was near death.

Luckily, a group of aid workers found him and took him to a hospital camp. The camp was filled with other people who were suffering from the effects of the drought. Cedric was given food and water, and he started to regain his strength.

As Cedric recovered, he learned that he was now an orphan. There was no one left in the world who was related to him. He was taken to an orphanage, where he would live with other children who had also lost their families.

Cedric was scared and sad, but he was grateful to be alive. He started to make new friends at the orphanage and he learned that he was not alone in the world.

The drought in Uganda continued for many more months, but eventually, the rains came and the people were able to start rebuilding their lives. Cedric grew up in the orphanage, but he never forgot the hardship and heartbreak he had experienced during the drought. He became a strong and resilient young man, and he dedicated his life to helping others who were in need.

The Heatwave

The sun blazed down mercilessly on the city of Delhi, India. The heat was intense and unrelenting, and the people of the city were struggling to keep cool. They sought refuge in air-conditioned buildings, drank cool drinks, and used fans to try and beat the heat.

For days, the heatwave continued, with temperatures reaching record highs. People started to become sick, and hospitals were overwhelmed with heat-related illnesses. Despite the efforts of the government to keep the people cool, the death toll was rising.

Sana, a young woman in her twenties, was struggling to make ends meet. She lived in a small, cramped apartment with her husband and their two young children. With no air-conditioning, they were at the mercy of the scorching heat.

"This heat is killing us," Sana's husband, Ahmed, said as they lay in bed one night, sweating despite the fan blowing directly on them. "We need to find a way to cool down."
Sana knew her husband was right. They needed to find a way to keep themselves and their children cool, or they would fall victim to the heatwave like so many others had.

Sana and Ahmed started to search for ways to stay cool. They visited public parks and pools, but they were overcrowded with people seeking refuge from the heat. They tried to stay in air-conditioned shopping malls as much as possible, but they couldn't afford to spend all day there.

One day, they heard about a community center that was providing free air-conditioning and water to those affected by the heatwave. They hurried over, eager for some relief from the heat. When they arrived, they were greeted by volunteers handing out cool drinks and fans. The air-conditioning was a godsend, and for the first time in days, Sana and her family felt cool and refreshed.

Despite their best efforts, tragedy struck. Sana's daughter became ill from the heat, and she was rushed to the hospital. Despite the efforts of the doctors and nurses, she did not survive.
Sana was devastated. She had lost her daughter to the heatwave, and she felt helpless and alone. She and Ahmed stayed by their daughter's side, crying and holding her hand until it was time to say goodbye.

The heatwave finally started to ease, and the people of Delhi started to pick up the pieces of their lives. But for Sana and Ahmed, life would never be the same. They had lost their daughter, and the memory of her would always be with them.

In the weeks and months that followed, Sana and Ahmed started to find ways to cope with their loss. They started to volunteer at the community center, helping others who were affected by the heatwave. They found comfort in helping others, and they knew that their daughter would be proud of them.

The heatwave in India was a tragedy, but it also brought the people of Delhi together. They supported each other and worked together to overcome the challenges they faced. And through it all, they remembered the loved ones they had lost, and they honored their memory by helping others in need.

Printed in Great Britain
by Amazon

45787313R00020